Thirty Paths to Silence

As always these labours of love are dedicated to all those seekers of that still small voice within, that which is.

This is the third handbook in a companion set. Thirty basic simple visualisations, which have been tried and tested on my own students, therefore Thirty Paths is dedicated to all those who are continually seeking that still small voice within, that which is.

What started as a simple handbook has taken me on a wonderful, completely different journey, and for this I thank you.

The small children's section was inspired by the arrival of a grandson, so I have to dedicate this section to

Burty Johnson with love

August 2005

Thirty Paths to Silence

Written and devised by Susan Johnson

Designed by The Art Room
Some Photography by David Johnson

Printed in England by CP Offset Limited, Darlington.
Telephone 01325 462315
e-mail: production@cpo.octacon.co.uk
First printed and published August 2005

Published by Susan Johnson
© Susan Johnson 2005
E-mail: susan@thirtypaths.com
website: www.thirtypaths.com

ARTS COUNCIL ENGLAND

Contents

Yoga Nidra

Yoga Nidra precedes visualisation. Before we start to imagine, the body must be totally relaxed. Begin the relaxation technique by allowing the body to totally let go.

Feel the body sinking into the mat, allow the shoulders to spread across the floor, move the head from side to side to release the neck, allow the head to let go. Imagine a cool blue light surrounding your body from the crown of the head to the tips of the toes, feel this light widening outwards, creating an aura of light around you. Feel it pulsating with life and energy, allow this light to be a healing light, if you feel in need of healing either mentally, emotionally, or physically allow this healing to take place whilst you relax.

Take the attention to the breath and allow the belly to slowly rise and fall with each breath, do not try and alter the breath in any way just witness the in and out, the flow, the slow coming and going, the evenness, the quiet rhythm. Allow the body to just be.

Now you are aware of melting down onto the floor, and you feel quite safe and secure,feel the colour blue soaking into the body, drenching all your cells with fresh life force, with energy, with balance, allow yourself to surrender to the healing.

Now take the attention to the feet, and allow the toes to spread and separate. Turn the toes inwards, flex and release, allow the instep to let go, the sole of the foot, the ankle, and feel the feet as solid and heavy, feel as though the feet are moving away from you, dense and heavy so heavy that you feel as though you are unable to move them. Allow the feet to relax and let go, feel them flopping out to the side. Allow the legs to release, the shins, the calfs, the knee and the kneecap, the thigh and the back of the thigh, allow the legs to release and let go, feel as though the legs are moving away from you solid, heavy and dense. Take the attention to the hands, to the back of the hand touching the floor, to the fingertips, the fingers and the palm of the hand, feel the softness in the palm of the hand, allow the lower arm to let go, the elbow, the upper arm, the whole of the arm releasing down, moving away.

Take the attention to the back and feel the vertebrae release from the base of the spine to the crown of the head visualise each vertebrae letting go and release onto the floor. Feel the whole of the back spread outwards, feel the back widen,at the same time feel the length, the stretch, the whole of the back spreading across the floor, and be aware of the amount of space the body takes up, the small amount of space.

Take the visualisation to the belly and be aware of the softness in the belly, the slow steady breath, the calm quiet coming and going of the breath, witness the rhythm, the separation of the breath, the pause, and the still point, feel as if the whole body is breathing, that the breath is breathing the body.

Allow the abdomen to let go and feel the softness in the belly, allow the chest centre to open out and on each inhalation feel the division of the breath, allow this openness to create a space within the chest centre allowing you the freedom to breathe mentally and physically, allow this freedom to open out the heart centre creating a releasement, a feeling you may not have felt for a long time, allow this centre to be filled with peace.

Feel this openness now spreading to the throat to release the voice, to move around the neck, the back of the head, the crown of

the head, the scalp, the space between the scalp and the skull, and even the hair on the head.

As you allow the face to let go and soften, the lower jaw slightly drops, feel the entire face release, the forehead, the eyes, the eyebrows, the eyelids relaxing in pools of darkness, the temples, the nose, the tip of the nose, the cheeks, the cheekbones, the upper lip and the lower lip, the jaw and the hinges of the jaw, the chin and even the ears and earlobes.

Feel the whole body release and sink down onto the floor all you are aware of is the steady breath, the rise and fall of the belly as the breath moves in and out, the stillness, the journey to visualisation.

Sitting Relaxation

This is one of my students favourite relaxation techniques, we sometimes do it instead of Yoga Nidra and then lie down on the mat for our deep relaxation.

Sit in an upright position and feel the base of the spine comfortable. Feel the sits bones connecting with the mat and lengthen up through the base of the spine, feel as though you are being gently raised and lengthened like a cord, allow the rib cage to expand and widen and feel the back opening out.

Make sure the shoulders are released and not held. Now become aware of the breathing and feel the body now releasing. Focus into the eyebrow centre. Take a few minutes to allow the breathing to become even, allowing yourself to merge into the sound and feel of the breath.

Slowly start to drop the head, allowing the chin to gently dip into the throat. As the head releases you feel the length in the neck and this lengthening of the neck is relaxing, feel as though the neck is unwinding an inch at a time, begin to feel any unusual sounds, feel the neck as though it is unravelling like a taut length of cord, the tension is flowing out of it, this cord is now released and free and is beginning to lower your head forward. Feel the head curl downwards and still you feel there is more to unwind, in fact your neck feels so free your head is almost touching your upper chest.

Now you begin to feel the shoulders release as your head moves further downwards, your upper back is relaxed, the middle of the back, and still you feel you can go further. Take the attention to the base of the spine and feel the whole of the back beginning to curl downwards, until your head is almost resting in your lap, the weight of your head is drawing you down, and still you feel the body relaxing, it feels good, comfortable, the back is now rounded, the belly soft, the neck long and relaxed without any strain, and all you are aware of is the stillness, the movement of the breath the total relaxation, the point of stillness, complete relaxation. Stay in that position for a few minutes, completely at ease and relaxed.

As you begin to uncurl, start the unwinding from the base of the spine, keep the chin into the throat, feel the lower back return, the middle of the back, the upper back, the nape of the neck, be aware of the release of the chin lock as you bring the neck up. Slowly raise the chin up towards the ceiling, compressing the neck, feeling the complete stretch, chin pointing towards the ceiling, and then return to centre. Come into the eyebrow centre, observe how you feel, sit in silence for a few more minutes to allow the body to readjust.

Caution; Observe contraindications for neck and head

Water

Visualise a trickling stream.
A stream running through a green meadow.
A meandering river.

A swollen river seeping up the riverbank.
A river tumbling over rocks.
Rapids.
A wide swirling river
A river leading into an estuary.
A harbour.
A river merging with the sea.
A restless sea.
A stormy sea.
Seahorses
A heavy swell
Waves lashing against the seashore.
A calm sea
A tranquil sea
The sea leading back to the harbour.
A wide river

A lazy, quiet river
Rock Pools
A river beginning to narrow
A river going upwards towards a gorge.
A series of tumbling waterfalls.
A cascading waterfall,

and as you look at this waterfall you see all the colours of the rainbow glistening in the sunlight, the colours jump out like sparks, blue sparkles, pink and pale green, as you stand there imagine this rainbow waterfall flowing over you now, and as it does it cleanses, dredges, and clears your entire system, it rebalances your body, renews and heals, feel your body now how free you feel, how clean, how pure, completely free from toxins.

Rest for a while before you come out of your visualisation.

The Five Resolves

The five resolves can be used at that point during relaxation when the mind is alert but the body rests. Affirmations and resolves are direct commands to the mind. The affirmations can be changed weekly or to suit. To enhance the technique I have used pebbles as the tool for each resolve.

I have chosen;
I know no fear.
  The colour of the pebble is red.
I am brave.
  The colour of the pebble is deep mauve.
I am strong.
  The colour of the pebble is blue.
I am healthy.
  The colour of the pebble is green.
I am improving day by day.
  The colour for the pebble is golden yellow.

When you have completed Yoga Nidra begin the visualisation.

Imagine you have in your left hand five pebbles. Each pebble represents an affirmation.

Begin the visualisation by transferring from the left hand to the right hand the red pebble, as you transfer the pebble repeat to yourself the affirmation, I know no fear, as you hold it in the palm of your hand repeat twice, I know no fear.

Transfer from the left hand to the right hand the deep mauve pebble, as you transfer the pebble repeat to yourself the affirmation I am brave, as you hold it in the palm of your hand repeat the affirmation twice, I am brave.

Transfer from the left hand to the right hand the blue pebble as you transfer the pebble repeat to yourself the affirmation, I am strong, as you hold it in the palm of your hand repeat the affirmation twice, I am strong.

Transfer from the left hand to the right the green pebble, as you transfer the pebble repeat to yourself the affirmation, I am healthy, as you hold it in the palm of your hand repeat the affirmation twice, I am healthy.

Transfer the last pebble from the left hand to the right the golden yellow pebble, as you transfer the pebble repeat to yourself the affirmation, I am improving day by day, as you hold it in the palm of your hand repeat the affirmation twice, I am improving day by day.

Now you have the five pebbles in your right hand, repeat once again the five affirmations.

Rotation of Consciousness

Following relaxation the student follows the voice, and visualises the object or idea.

Lie still, lying on a soft blue velvet blanket,
Sinking deeper, feeling secure,
Feeling at ease, releasing,
Feeling the body soften, melting, melting down, deep into relaxation
Releasing, allowing the body to let go, to feel the entire body surrender
I have all I need at this moment in time
Time is not important
I am where I am at this moment in time
I am in my centre, I am relaxed
I am free, free to be, free to be who I am now, at this moment in time,
At this precious moment in time,
I am completely free.

Allow the breath to breathe the body, to feel the vibration, to be aware of the still point, to be mindful of the pause, to allow the waves of relaxation to flow, to allow the breath to breathe the body.

I am happy at this moment in time
I feel good within
I am where I am
I am pleased with myself, with my achievements, I honour myself, I respect myself
Deep down I know myself
Deep down I know my limitations, because I am human

Deep down I can communicate with my inner self, because this is where I am
This is where I want to be. In my calm centre, within.

This is where I feel safe, this is where I feel secure, this is where I feel as though I have come home.

This is where I touch my divine source, such is the depth of that unconditional love, it almost takes my breath away.

Meditation On An Apple

Meditation is made that much easier by getting the students to bring an object to focus on. The path to Meditation must begin with concentration and contemplation. You cannot meditate if you are unable to sit. First cultivate the position and gradually build up. Ask the students to bring an apple.

Start the practice. Place on the floor in front of you the apple. Begin the Meditation in a sitting posture that you feel comfortable with, if you cannot sit with the back straight, sit back to back with a partner, on a chair or lean against the wall. Be aware of the sits bones on the floor, the length in the spine, the relaxed shoulders, the open chest. The back of the wrists rest on the knees and the first finger of each hand is bent and touches the thumb, (chin Mudra) this hand gesture helps to create a spiritual mood.

Begin to observe the breath, feel the belly loosen, the chest and shoulders open, and create space in the heart chamber, observe the movement of the breath, the sound, the vibration, the feelings of relaxation, stay alert. Look at the apple in front of you, observe the texture, is the skin well polished? Study the apple closely, its size, shape, condition, texture, colouring, see how the apple is not just one colour but several shades of green, yellow, pink, red, maybe russet. See how the apple has been ripened by the sun, part of the apple may have been in the shade, the apple may have marks or bruises where it fell, imagine it falling onto the orchard grass. Does your apple still have a stalk intact or a label of the country of origin?

Now take the apple in your hands, smell it, feel the coolness, imagine how juicy it tastes, feel it against your cheek, does it feel rough or smooth, even or uneven, round or misshapen. Now place the apple down again and keep your gaze focused steady upon it. Now visualise the apple tree, how it grew from a pip, until now it is a fully mature tree laden with apples in the orchard. All the apples vary in shades of colour, how they all ripen at different stages as the sun catches them. Now imagine your apple dropping from the tree onto the orchard floor, and the journey it took to get to you, until you eventually bought it.

The Golden Fingers

This is a healing meditation working with a partner. Begin the meditation sitting back to back with a partner. Place the hands in the lap with the palms facing upwards ready to receive. Lengthen the back to allow for the free flow of energy and adjust the shoulders to widen and open out the chest. Become aware of your partner's breathing, feel the vibration, the movement of the breath, how the breath is adjusting, beginning to slow down, be aware of the rhythm, the flow, the rise and fall of the chest, the stillness and the calmness as your partner begins to settle into their own centre.

Now take your attention to your own breathing and notice how you have become still and have relaxed into the rhythm of the breath, how the breath brings a balance, an equilibrium, you feel as though you are almost breathing in synchrony. Be aware of the inhalation, the pause and the exhalation, focus on the whole cycle of the breath.

Now begin to feel a warmth spreading around your lower back, feel it rising around the middle of the back, around the shoulders until the whole of your back feels warm.

Now take the attention to the hands in the lap which now feel warm and tingling, imagine the finger tips now pulsating with golden energy as if golden threads are hanging from the finger tips weighing them down, feel the golden energy move into the fingers and into the palms of the hands, until your hands are vibrating with golden

energy, radiating healing, feel your hands soften and prepare to take them to your belly, your solar plexus, as you do this transfer, begin to deepen the breath allowing the belly to rise and fall as you receive the energy. Let the belly soften, widen and spread as you take in all this golden light energy.

Now allow the chest and the heart centre to open, as you do this feel space and freedom in the heart centre, allow yourself to become the giver unconditionally.

Continue to breathe focusing now on your partner. Now visualise giving this healing energy to your partner. Transfer firstly trust, upliftment, healing for body, mind and emotions, contentment, peace and tranquillity, support and friendship. Ask for the universal energy to go where it is needed.

Take a couple of minutes to exchange this healing. When you feel ready open the eyes and relax.

Pranayama The Breath Of Life

The following practices of breathing exercises help the student to demystify Pranayama. They are simple and effective and take up about 15 minutes in the usual Yoga class but it is essential to incorporate them.

Certain points to remember
Remind students to bring tissues each week.
Breathing is always through the nose.
Never strain or hold the breath.
Get in touch with your own personal breathing rhythm.
Watch, observe and witness the flow of the breath.
If you ever feel discomfort or dizzy stop the practice.

The Following are a selection of easy to follow breathing exercises.

Breathing in Tadasan

Inhale through the nose.
Exhale through the mouth.

Stand in Tadasan. Feet firmly on the ground, feel earthed and at ease. Allow the earth to support your body, but if you feel imbalanced adjust the feet. Let the knees soften, lengthen out of the waist, open out the chest centre, create some space around and under the rib cage, drop the shoulders, lengthen the neck, allow the head to feel as if it is being drawn up by a length of string .

Close the eyes. Place the hands on the hips. Draw the chest up then press the hip bones with the hands in a downward direction, space will be created and air will come into the lungs.

Keep the nostrils wide so that you inhale the maximum amount of air. Breathe in the breathing is full and deep. Keep the chest fully open, the abdomen relaxed, the spine and neck straight. Remember do not draw the shoulders up, do not draw the abdomen in, never force.

To exhale, place the hands on the upper ribcage and feel the rib cage sink down gradually to the lower rib cage then the abdomen.

Brahmari or Humming Bee Breath

Sit in a relaxed meditation position. Padmasana, (the lotus) or Vajrasana Thunderbolt pose or any sitting position that is comfortable for you.

Make sure the back is straight, the abdomen lifted and the chest is open to allow the free flow of Prana throughout the body. Do not strain or try to alter the natural rhythm of the breath.

Begin by becoming aware of the natural breath, feel the breath coming in through the nostrils, the warmth or coolness, the length of the inhalation and exhalation, the pause, the free flow, compare each nostril, the movement as the breath moves into the chest. Allow the rib cage to expand, and be conscious of the width of the chest.

Use the index finger of each hand to close the flap over the ears, this internalises the sound and intensifies the effects. Inhale through both nostrils; slightly constrict the glottis to make a gentle deep breathing sound.

Exhale slowly through both nostrils, again slightly constricting the glottis, to make a low melodious sound like a female Bee humming. Repeat at least six times.

Lower the hands when you are finished, keeping the eyes closed and listen to the echo resonate throughout the head and chest. Sit quietly for a few moments.

The Benefits of Brahmari

Relaxation, the sound penetrates deep into the mind and body, drawing the attention inwards the sound creating a Mantra. It brings calmness both physically and mentally. Helps promote restful sleep.

Very beneficial for the vocal chords and a popular exercise for singers and speakers.

Eases a sore throat and mild ear infections.

Directing The Energy

I find these little 10 minute exercises useful during the Yoga class.

Count 10 for inhalation, count three to transfer the fingertips, count 10 for exhalation.

Repeat up to 10 times.

1. Lie on the back, eyes closed and rest the fingertips on the belly, slowly inhale to 10 and visualise golden energy being drawn from the solar plexus into the fingertips.

2. Continue to the count of 3 to transfer the fingertips to the forehead, exhale to 10 as you visualise golden energy being drawn into the forehead. Hold the forehead firmly.
3. Return the fingertips to the belly.
4. Repeat.
5. Now you can take the energy to any part of the body on the exhalation.
6. Concentration is essential in this exercise.

This exercise is best done prior to relaxation when the lights are dim, as some students may be a bit self conscious.

Breathe The Difference

This is a simple Pranayama practice to discover the feelings that arise with different breathing techniques. It is especially good for beginners in class as they get instant results.

It is best practiced lying down prior to relaxation. Allow at least 15 minutes. Discuss later.

Begin by taking the attention to the brow centre and encourage the mind to come into a point of stillness. Focus, allow any thoughts to come and go, just witness them, observe, try not to get into any conversation with the mind.

Now be aware of the breath, the inhalation, the pause, the exhalation and the still point, be aware of the length of the inhalation and the exhalation, notice the even rhythm, the smoothness, does the breath feel warm or cool? Is it moving up the nostrils easily or impeded. If the breath feels at all ragged or rushed let it be, do not try and alter the breathing.

Place the hands on the solar plexus and connect to your centre, feel the movement as your fingers separate with the movement of the breath, feel the abdomen opening out, spreading, releasing, unwinding, feel the breath beginning to slow down. Listen in to your internal vibrations as the solar plexus becomes engaged and energised.

Now be aware of any sensations you are feeling in the belly, any emotions, anything at all, just observe what is happening in the solar plexus.

Now draw the breath up into the heart chamber, and as you do, allow the chest centre to open out, widen and spread. Feel the shoulders expand together with the whole of the back, release onto the floor as the chest centre opens. Breathe, now continue breathing slowly and gently and as you do you begin to feel space, an openness, a complete surrender, letting go allows your heart centre to open out and in this opening you can now draw up from deep down in this energy centre freedom, You are now free.

Be aware of any sensations you are now feeling in the heart centre, any emotions, anything at all, just observe the difference as you connect into the heart. Allow yourself to feel anything, the heart will always be truthful. You are now in touch with your heart centre and working through any blockages that may be holding you back. Breathe in the difference and embrace yourself.

Now is a good time to repeat your own affirmation and resolves.

As we move up the Chakras they become more refined, therefore our feelings and emotions are also refined.

Winter Walk

Imagine yourself going for a walk along the river bank on a cold frosty day.

The air is fresh and clear and there is a stillness around you. A heavy frost has dusted the bushes and trees. Ahead of you the trees are laden with what looks like icing, they are thick with white frost. The frost has created all sorts of unusual patterns and shapes, the grasses look striped, the tightly curled up ferns resemble snails in their shells, the berries are covered in cold ice, the earth is hard beneath your feet as you start to walk along the path.

The mud and pools on the path are solid and glassy and your footsteps crunch into the hard ice. You walk along beside the gentle flowing river, in places on the river bank the water has frozen, thick and wedges of ice cling to the banks, a trickle of water continues to erode the sides, but it is hard to penetrate and the shade keeps it frozen. You continue along the path looking at the beauty of the woods and the whiteness around you, how maybe in a few days the scene will have changed and you will be unable to recapture the beauty.

You soon find yourself climbing upwards towards what used to be an old Summer House, and you take a seat inside, you are quite high up in the woods now and you can see the river flowing gently down, the picture resembles a Christmas Card, you are in complete isolation, you cannot see any habitation or people.

Suddenly your eye catches movement and you slowly look towards the left, two small deer are standing together just by the edge of a clearing in the path, they are so young, brown with a white patch on their hind, and they look up directly at you as if startled. They are so close, you have to hold your breath, and then they are gone.

You move further upwards now and you find yourself beside a small waterfall, the icicles are hanging freely, some are like spears, sharp and long, some are twisted. Sheets of ice drip down off a large boulder, the rocks are covered in ice and have frozen encrusted moss and lichen, even the plants and foliage have been frozen in time. The pool beneath the waterfall is partially frozen, the ice cold water is so clear and it is the shade of aquamarine. The water falls, and moves differently as the volume has been diminished, the sound as it falls into the pool is quieter, less dramatic, peaceful. It trickles down the hillside and as you move on the sound is gone.

Soon you come out onto a plateau and you are in front of a small tarn, the water has turned to solid ice and in places cracks are appearing at the edges, leaves, sticks, logs and bracken have been frozen as they lay, and there is no sign of moving water.

You sit down on a fallen tree and just listen to the sound of the stillness, silence, nothing moves, not even a bird, the day is beginning to darken, it is late afternoon. The sky is clouding over and maybe there is a snow shower on the way, you are aware that nature is sleeping, all is warm beneath the earth, all is taken care of, all is well and all is well.

Winter

Beginning in the New Year, this is a time for fresh beginnings, a new start, a time of making resolves and resolutions. Allow the past to go, we cannot change it in any shape or form, but we can create our future. This is the time of reflection, not holding on to the past, of waiting, and allowing the Universe to direct us, to be still, and in that quiet waiting come changes, allow the Universe to be the guide to your dreams. When you are unable to make that decision, and you have done your best, hand it over to a higher source and wait. For it is in being still and waiting that what we need, not what we want, unfolds. This is the time to look forward, to make goals.

The Affirmation is:
I believe in myself.
I believe in my capabilities.
I believe in my own inner strength.
I believe in my goals.
My still inner voice is my own Guru.
I have no need to go elsewhere.

Visualise:
The hard cold earth.
Deep snow.
Footprints in the deep snow.
Pine trees, branches laden with ice and snow.
Snow capped hills.
Holly and Ivy.
A Christmas Rose.
A robin on a branch.
Frosted grass and ferns.
The slow trickle of water.
Icicles hanging from the riverbank.
A Frozen pond.
Twigs and logs set in icy water.
A frozen waterfall.
A boat moored on a frozen lake.
The white blanket all around.
The clearness of the light.
The steady sound of your feet.
The stillness around you.
The Earth sleeping.
The sound of the Universe, The sound of OM.

Springtime Meditation

Springtime, the time when the days brighten up, the nights are lighter, and all around is growth. The trees are beginning to show their leaves, and the new grass feels spongy beneath our feet, we see the plants pushing forward at a rapid pace, the harsh cold dark days of winter are coming to an end. Now the moon is powerful, the spring tides are mountainous, they rush in on the March breeze bringing boats battling to a safe harbour, they churn up the sea bed and rearrange the sand, pebbles are redistributed in heaps against the sea wall. Bales of seaweed are scattered along the shoreline, and all kinds of sea life have to be well anchored to their homes.

In the countryside new lambs are being born, the hills green up, wild flowers peep from crevices, daffodils and spring flowers bloom in clumps, the rivers run smooth and clear, as the snow melts off the mountains. The early April showers bring that warm drink to the cold earth. This is the time of hope, expectations, planning. New life-force and energy lift our spirits, and because we are also part of this natural cycle, we change.

Visualise:
A Full Moon.
A Mountainous Sea.
A lone Yacht battling for Harbour.
Snow Capped Mountains.
A Cascading Waterfall.
A Bright green field of fresh Spring grass.
Lambs grazing.
Clumps of daffodils.
April showers.
A steady shower of warm Spring rain.

A torrential downpour.
The heat rising off the earth.
A perfect rainbow.
A mountain Path.
Climbing up the mountain path.
The stones beneath your feet.
The sun on your back.
The view from the ridge.
The top of the mountain.
The safe cairn to shelter.
The view all around.
The feeling of achievement.
The feeling of strength.
The freedom of the mountain top.
The communication with your own inner self.

Seven Steps To Freedom

This Meditation is to balance and bring you in touch with the Chakras. Lying completely still and relaxed but staying alert.

Be aware of the seven Chakras and where they are positioned. We are going to access them by colour, symbol and Mantra.

Start the exercise by taking the attention to the base of the spine, here we have the colour red, visualise a deep crimson red at the base of the spine. It is the earth element, this energy centre grounds you, the elephant symbolises stability and solidarity. The mantra is Lam. Repeat the Mantra Lam three times.

Lying a little above the root centre is One's own abode the second Chakra, usually seen as the colour between red and orange. The element is water, the symbol is a crocodile, and the Mantra is Wam. This centre has the deep rooted primitive instinct of man, by refining this centre we rise above fear. Repeat the Manta Wam three times.

The third Chakra is the solar plexus known as the fire centre, the focal point of heat, the colour is bright yellow, the symbol is the ram and the mantra is Ram, when the energy moves up the Chakras it becomes transformed and refined through this centre Repeat the mantra Ram three times.

The fourth Chakra is the heart centre. This is where we connect with sound, the pulse of the body, the vibration, The space within the chamber of the heart, creates the ability to resonate and echo. The colour is Emerald Green, the symbol is a swift black antelope, and the element is air, the Mantra is Yam. Repeat the Mantra Yam three times.

The fifth Chakra is at the throat centre this centre influences the vocal cords, the voice, and communication. The colour is Smokey violet, the symbol is a pure white elephant, the element is ether and the Mantra is Ham. Repeat the Mantra Ham three times.

The sixth Chakra is the third eye, the centre of the forehead. This centre is really where we are now in our development, we cannot open this centre until all the others have become refined. It is through this centre that we can receive guidance, and intuition, It is the concentration centre in meditation and the focus point for concentration and contemplation. The negative and positive flow of prana converge at this centre creating awareness. The colour is grey or white, and the Mantra is the sacred sound of Aum. Repeat the sacred sound of Aum three times.

The crown of the head is the seat of consciousness and the path to liberation and enlightenment.

If you want to end the exercise on a chant you can repeat the six Mantras three times each this would help to stabilise and cement the practice.

Lam, Lam, Lam, - Wam, Wam, Wam, Ram, Ram, Ram, - Yam, Yam, Yam, Ham, Ham, Ham, - Aum, Aum, Aum.

Om Shanti

The Green Room

When we think of the colour green, we connect to the chest centre, green symbolises calmness, Prana, vitality, and life force. We experience the changing nature of the breath and the transformation. Green is a natural healing colour which connects us to nature and we naturally think of respiration and oxygen, this encourages us to breathe with more awareness. In the deepening of the breath we feel the chest centre opening out and this gives us freedom and space.

Start your relaxation by following the Yoga Nidra.

Imagine you are walking towards a large green door, as you approach this door, persuade yourself, you are going into a room filled with peace, harmony, and calmness. Give yourself this time to unwind, relax and allow the mind to feel free to wander into the visualisation.

You now enter the room and you immediately feel the coolness and calmness. The walls are painted a cool peppermint, the ceiling and cornice a pastel shade of green, the carpet is a deep emerald green, the curtains and the couch a heavy brocade of deep forest, the cushions are soft and large and they almost invite you to lie down. A heavy chintz throw drapes over the arm and you feel drawn towards the couch.

You lay down a while and allow the cushions to take all your weight, you sink down into the softness feeling the body mould into the cushion, look at all the different shades of green, the pale pastel, the deep heavy forest and the bright emerald. How all these shades blend, mix, melt, and fuse into each other, the light filters into the room and shafts of sunlight create different shades. You feel the colour green surround you, move around your aura, enfold you, breathe into the colour green now, and feel the tranquillity it brings, the balance, the harmony, the deep, calming, even, rhythm of the breath as it slows down to a steady pace, and you feel yourself drifting, melting, into the soft, cushions. You feel supported and completely relaxed.

I am at ease, I am content, I am where I am at this moment in time and all is well. This moment is all there is, is all I need, Give up all that you are holding on to and allow the chest centre to expand, allow the rib cage to widen, create space for movement, feel the freedom as a new experience comes into your heart centre.

I accept that when my heart is open I am moving from the right place. Now feel the breath exchanging energy, I am releasing negative thought, I am accepting positive thought, I am renewing my life-force, I am creating healing. My thoughts are now directing this healing Prana to all areas of my body, mind or emotions that may be in need at this moment in time. I am directly in charge of my thought patterns.

Now I am beginning to feel stronger, because I have complete control of my thoughts, I am now focused on inner strength, purpose, I am ready to live life.

The Stone Circle

Lying in Shavasana prepare the body for relaxation. Feel the entire body let go to the experience of deep relaxation, this is achieved by deepening the breath, and allowing the body to become heavy, solid and dense, allow the earth to support and hold you, it cannot let you go, give yourself the opportunity to surrender to the moment.

Visualise yourself standing in the centre of 8 standing stones. These are no ordinary standing stones they are all precious gems and they are huge. They all have their own power, vibration and life energy. As you stand in the centre of these stones you can feel different energies.

In front of you stands 'Ruby' a beautiful red Gem, rich and full of healing for all mental health problems. It is also the heart stone as it encourages selfless service and spiritual devotion. It is connected to the first Chakra and dispels fear. Therefore embrace it. Visualise yourself now touching this precious gem.

The second gemstone is 'Moonstone' a translucent feldspar with a white and pink sheen. The solid Mother Earth and friend of all females. It balances Ying and Yang. It is connected to the second and sixth Chakra. When you embrace Moonstone you are embracing yourself. Visualise yourself now touching this precious gem.

Next stands 'Amber, The mindful one'. This Gem is so called because it remembers the past and is the resin of ancient trees.

Amber is good for memory and the endocrine system, it also helps the mind find the soul, This Gem is connected to the solar plexus, therefore embrace it. Visualise yourself now touching this precious gem.

The fourth Gemstone is 'Emerald' the unconditional love stone, a deep green pulsating with strength for the heart Chakra. This is the friend of the seeker, it holds the power to heal, therefore embrace it. Visualise yourself now touching this precious gem.

The fifth gemstone is 'Lapis Lazuli' a beautiful blue flecked stone. 'The Night Stone a powerful relaxant for the mind and body. Good for communication with the higher self. It was said that King Solomon wore this on his breastplate for protection. Opens the throat and the brow centre. Therefore embrace it. Visualise yourself now touching this precious gem.

The sixth gemstone is 'Amethyst,' 'the elevator' deep mauve; it strengthens the entire immune system and is an exceptional blood cleanser. A very powerful aid in meditation by bringing the lower natures to a higher consciousness. Connected to the sixth and seventh Chakra Therefore embrace it. Visualise yourself now touching this precious gem.

The seventh gemstone to touch is the 'Quartz Clear', one of the highest crystals, good for the soul, good for healing, the complete balancer, and grounder. The Meditator's friend. Opens out the crown

Chakra. Therefore embrace it. Visualise yourself now touching this precious gem.

As you turn you face 'Jasper, The Talisman'. Healers have used this stone for centuries, a gemstone of many colours. A powerful healer for the entire body, the perfect grounder. Jasper gives you what you need and supports and balances any Chakra

Therefore embrace it. Visualise yourself now touching this precious stone.

You have received from these energies all that you need, take a moment to reflect.

Be aware of yourself back now in your own place, fully relaxed, recharged, rebalanced and at ease.

Step Into The Pyramid

Allow the body now to let go into a state of complete relaxation, feel the body heavy, solid, dense, allow the back to widen, to feel the shoulders spread, and as the shoulders spread, so the neck releases, allowing the head to feel heavy, give the head away to a soft velvet cushion, feel this cushion supporting your head, holding it, taking the weight whilst you relax.

Feel the entire body now sinking onto a bed of golden soft sand, feel the warmth as your body moulds into place, feel the ease, the comfort, the desire to now completely let go. Listen to the sound of your breath as it slows down, as the heart beat relaxes, as your internal organs relax, as you allow the breath to breathe the body, feel the sounds of the universe through the sand, the vibration of the universe, the sound of AUM.

That sacred sound of AUM is your Mantra as you sink deeper into a state of equilibrium.

Visualise the Desert and a huge Step Pyramid, you are walking towards this Pyramid, how mighty it must have looked freshly built, how the sandstone must have glistened, how the steps must have been sharp and precise, every edge cleanly cut shining in the sun, how high, the complete triangle at each side, this sacred place built with the afterlife in mind, the Egyptian Mystery.

You walk towards the steps, some have crumbled away. How many feet have walked this stairway, have moved around the very place where you are now placing your feet? The sandstone is weathered and eroded by harsh sand storms and time, the sun casts shadows and picks out the different shades and textures of stone. The crumbling steps lead towards a door which stands ajar, and you walk towards it, imagining the ancient race of Pharaoh, rituals, worship of Gods, hieroglyphics, Astronomy, amazing story tellers.

You walk through the door and find yourself in the main chamber, all the walls are covered in writings, paintings, hieroglyphics. They tell the stories of battles, famines, afterlife, Queens and Pharaoh, all spoken in pictures, you look up towards the ceiling and the ceiling is deep indigo blue, painted stars and moons glisten in the semi dark chamber. You marvel at the intelligence.

You have brought with you a small velvet bag which holds a pink quartz crystal, this is your own personal crystal which you alone use, you are going to charge this crystal with energy from this great pyramid. Open the drawstring of the velvet bag and take out the crystal, hold it in your hand. How does it feel? Is it cool or warm? feel the texture and the shape, visualise the colour, the healing shade of pink, hold it, now feel a gentle warmth, a heat generating, a gentle energy beginning to build up. Feel the potency building, the power. Take three deep breaths. Now ask for this crystal to be filled with a positive energy, Take three breaths. Now ask for this crystal to be filled with healing energy. Take three breaths. Now ask for this crystal to be filled with love. Take three deep breaths. Hold this moment, and now place the crystal back in the velvet bag.

Walking towards the open door you see the bright sun shining, each step down feeling more energy, more positive, more strength, more courage, healing, pulsating from your crystal in the velvet bag. Slowly returning from relaxation, deepen the breath, stretch, and feel your body once again supported by the earth, on your own mat, in your own place.
Om Shanti

The Precious Moment in Time

A Different Visualisation from the usual, the student is asked to look into a scene.

Visualise yourself looking into a very precious moment in time. You open a garden door to look into a walled garden. The garden is filled with old fashioned flowers, and the walls are covered in clematis, honeysuckle and old fashioned climbing roses, it is midsummer, and the day is hot and still. A huge blossom tree is still shedding its petals, they fall onto a large lawn, and onto a young lady who lies idly day-dreaming underneath the shade of the hanging branches, her thoughts private.

A baby lies in a pram besides her gurgling happily as the pink petals fall onto the canopy of the pram, she tries to catch them as they fall but they escape and flutter to the grass.

An old lady sits in her chair and simply observes the scene. She remembers well the very day, like yesterday when she bought that blossom tree, the young lady was but a girl when they carried the small sapling into the garden, and together they planted it. The garden was quite new then, but the old lady had a way with planting, she knew exactly where it should be.

The years went by and the tree grew and grew until it was now mature like herself, the garden established itself, the flowers matured, because she had spent her days shifting and moving plants into different positions to help them grow, and give them time to do their best, which they had. Her garden rewarded her every day when she walked around it, snipping here and encouraging there, sometimes she had to be ruthless and take out plants that seemed to smother their neighbours, but this was always done with the best of intentions.

Now she reflected that was exactly what she had done for the young lady lying there, she had tried to give her direction, had helped her grow and flourish in the best possible light, had never smothered her, had checked her with the best intentions, but she had also let her go and allowed her to experience her own experiences, and she reckoned that like her garden she had done a fine job.

The baby in the pram gurgled and smiled as the old lady bent to pick her up, what did life have in store for this little bundle she thought to herself, but she knew as her eyes met her daughter's that all was well. Between them they had the unbroken bond of unconditional love, and that knew no bounds.

The Body is A Miracle

Begin this relaxation by connecting to your physical body.

Become aware of the sensation of your back flat on the floor, feel the back as solid, and strong, visualise each vertebrae touching the floor, how flexible your back is, how it manages to support your whole frame, holding you upright, the mobility in the spine, how you can stretch, lengthen, turn and rotate, become a friend to your back, watch over it, learn how to rest it, nurture it, always work with your back in mind.

Now take your attention to your feet, feel how your feet earth you to the ground, connect you, they give you stability, and balance. Think of how many miles your feet walk in a lifetime, how they can climb rugged pathways, move through water, play games, dance in step, look to your feet and thank them for helping to walk you around this earth

Now feel the legs, the strength in the legs, how they help create movement and with the feet work endlessly day in and day out, creating all kinds of movements that we enjoy, but forget to thank them for.

Now feel the arms resting on the floor, the freedom we have with our arms, we hug and cuddle, we wave, hold and comfort, our arms are meant for embracing, they are our wings and have the exact span to hold another human being, the arms hold the shoulder to cry on, be grateful for this gift. Feel the hands now resting on the floor, the

fingers, how wonderful the hands are, we garden, drive, shop, and clean. The hands are free carrier bags. They touch, caress, feel, hold and heal, the hands grasp, grip, and shake, our hands are very precious to us and we thank them.

Feel the whole of the abdomen, how your belly holds for you the reserve of energy, of Prana and life force. How wonderful to feel sensations in the belly, of emotions, expectations, butterflies, how the belly connects you to all these senses and feelings and how through practice of Pranayama techniques the belly softens, releases and becomes your calm centre. How you feel the flow of the breath in the belly, delivering around your body a feeling of peace.

Now go in to the heart centre and be mindful of the sensations within the chamber, feel the freedom, the openness, the empathy and compassion that flows from this centre when it is unimpeded, how your heart has physically been beating all these years with ease. Draw into the love that is resting in this centre, the still inner voice, come into contact with yourself, your own relationship with yourself, that internal knowing, and how you are at this moment in time connecting with yourself. Your pathway is already clear, by intuition you know the way. Start to fall in love with your heart.

Feel the softness now in your face, how every muscle works for you, your face registers how you feel, the sun shines on it, the rain wets your skin, the cold chills your nose, tears run down your cheeks, age lines creep in, your eyes open and close, but your smile lights up your face, lights up a room, cheers the old lady passing by. Your face can be as welcoming as you choose, it identifies you, show it in the best possible light. For our unique face we are thankful.

Now allow the eyes to feel the sensation of darkness, our eyes are the most precious organs, they watch, sleep, see, and transfer these images and convert in less than the blink of a eye, we need to take very special care of our eyes, guard them fiercely.

And now the nose, the sensation of smell, which triggers memory, the smell of a newly opened rose, the skin of a baby, the fresh newly cut grass, the summer shower, these sacred and pleasant memories are evoked by smell. We honour and thank our bodies for continuing unconditionally to support and give us life. We give thanks from the heart.

Our physical bodies are this miracle of life and energy, what we cannot see is the biggest miracle, but we can feel it, sense it, receive it, embrace it, and believe it, the universal power and creator of all energy.

Om Shanti.

Moonlight Lovers

Go through the usual relaxation and Yoga Nidra.

Visualise yourself sitting beside a loch on a warm summer evening. The night is dark, the sky is deep velvet and a full moon is hiding behind the clouds. All is quiet and you are just observing the stillness of the night. The water is still on the loch, all is at peace.

Not far from the shore, alone on an island is a large crumbling castle, forgotten in the eons of time. The full moon creeps out from behind the clouds, and lights up the water, it creeps along creating a pathway to the castle. It gently and slowly begins to light up the castle, the windows, the buttresses, the remains of the stone walls, until you are able to see in the full moonlight, a castle that was once proud and sturdy. A moat surrounds the castle, and a drawbridge leads to the door.

The moon goes in and out of the clouds and the castle goes from light to darkness, an owl is hooting

and birds nesting in the walls seem disturbed, the full moon now lights up the water, creating a glistening sheen, it lights up the bridge and you see an Elizabethan lady standing on the bridge, waiting. Visualise her dress, her hat, her handkerchief in her hand how she twists it anxiously.

You are aware of the sound of horses hooves and you see her knight approaching the bridge. Visualise his clothes, his armour, the white horse as he gallops towards the lady, dismounts at the bridge and embraces her. You blink your eyes in disbelief, they are gone, locked in time together, moonlight lovers.

The Sea

Prepare yourself for your relaxation in the usual way

Imagine yourself lying on a beach on a warm summer's day. Feel yourself sinking down into soft golden sand, feel the body moulding into the sand, allow the warmth to spread around you, gently touching your face and creating a warm glow. Be aware of yourself drifting, melting and dissolving into a warm, relaxed state.

The tide is out and in front of you is a causeway that leads to an island, the island is totally cut off from the land when the tide comes in, but for now the tide is way out and it exposes not only the causeway but a ancient crossing marked by wooden poles, this crossing was used by pilgrims and monks in the olden times to get to the monastery on the island. Isolation and remoteness make this island a very safe haven.

The outgoing tide has uncovered rocks covered in seaweed, limpets and sea life and in the silence you can just faintly hear the sound of life moving around, a collective shifting. Your senses are now tuned in to movement and sound, the sea is as still as a mill pond, but in the distance you hear a gentle disturbance of waves, you see a fisherman in a small coble stop to draw up his lobster pots, he empties them and returns to the harbour. Further down the sands a man paints his boat, whilst a dog lies basking in the sun. A lone seagull perches on a rock, he is so close you can see the movement of his feathers as he plucks at himself, a yellow beady eye taking in the bait on offer. The sun glints on the sea creating a

moving shimmer of sparkling light. All is still and quiet.

The stillness is so peaceful, so restful, clouds drift by, looking up you identify shapes and images, changing shapes. Fluffy clouds drift by hanging like cotton wool, thin strands of cloud and then patches of blue. The blue reaches the horizon and merges to become an endless blue. You begin to feel yourself drifting, sinking deeper and deeper into a warm, peaceful state of relaxation, you feel yourself unwinding, and spreading into the golden sand, into a golden glow of warmth, finding now your own calm centre.

You are now completely at ease, safe, warm and comfortable. All you are aware of is the gentle lapping of the waves, as they go in and out, moving with quiet rhythm, just like your gentle breathing, even, slow and deep.

Feel yourself now connecting to the tranquillity, the peace, the solitude of the moment, in this moment you are at peace with yourself, you are at ease, there is no other time but this moment, and in this moment you have found the path to stillness.

The Crossroad

Crossroads represent junctions, decisions, and sometimes challenges, a crossroad is like a stopping place, a time to make a judgement. Sometimes it can become a learning curve on our journey, it can be a challenge but it will also be an experience.

The crossroad can be there for you to stop and just go with your instinct. When we approach the crossroad, sometimes it is best to let go and allow your inner self to make the journey and you follow. This is a visualisation with a difference.

Imagine you are approaching a crossroad; the signs are pointing left and right.

To the left is a path that appears long and straight, you cannot see too far into the distance but you feel the path is easy and straight forward.

To the right is a winding path that seems rather uneven and bumpy, it seems to wind up the hillside. You have to decide which path to choose. Take a few moments to decide your path.

Choose your path now, do not change it during the course of the visualisation.

We are now going to the left hand path, the road is long, straight and flat. On either side of the path are hedgerows, they are tall and obscure your view so you feel rather enclosed. All you can see ahead of you is the long road and it seems to stretch on and on. After a while you begin to feel rather tired, but you cannot find a place to sit as the hedgerows are unbroken and so you continue to walk on. Although the path is flat and straight it is uninteresting and you become bored with it.

In the distance you see another sign post, it leads off to the right, and takes you on a path through some meadows, you are surrounded by wild flowers, daisies, buttercups and bluebells, here seems a nice place to sit for a moment and reflect, so you lie down on the soft grass and allow yourself to let go and relax.

We are now going to the right hand path, this path is winding, and rather uneven and bumpy and it takes you up the side of a hillside which is a bit of a pull up, but it has the most wonderful open views, you can see all around. You feel invigorated, and because you can see for miles around, this gives you a sense of freedom, you can breathe and feel the energy.

The pathway leads down to a meadow, the grass looks fresh and new and the meadow is full of wild flowers daisies, buttercups and bluebells.

There seems to be a group of people lying on the grass.

When the students come out of the relaxation, discuss which path they took and why!

The Rose Garden

Take your time as you settle into a comfortable position for relaxation. Feel the body releasing, letting go, feeling heavy, dissolving into your calm centre. Breathe deeply and evenly, don't try and change the breath, just witness the flow, the still point and the pause. Feel the vibration of the breath as the body releases, unwinds, and gives, feel that calmness beginning to form within you, as you allow your body to be held, supported, you are safe, you are at ease, you are secure and all is well.

As you sink deep into your relaxed state you find yourself walking towards a walled garden on a warm summer day. A large oak door leads into a courtyard, and you open the door and enter a rose garden. The roses in this garden are crimson red and they are just waiting to burst into bloom. The perfume fills the air and almost takes your breath away. As you wander slowly around you are aware of the silence, all you can focus on is the scent, the colour, the bees and butterflies hovering, and in the distance the gentle sound of water trickling.

Walking down the courtyard path you stop to admire the most beautiful crimson red rose which has just opened. How the petals are tied neatly down against each other, the crinkled edge, the dew touching the rim, the perfect long stem, the perfect balance, and you feel in this moment your heart centre being touched by a wave of internal peace, by a sudden emotional feeling that you may not have felt for some time, but has just flowed over you, and for no other reason, than you have been touched by the miracle of life. The simplicity and humility of the moment have gently shifted any blockages that may have been held in the heart centre, and so you can move on now.

As you wander down the courtyard path you come across an old wall fountain hidden among the climbing roses, lichen and moss have covered the basin, a gentle trickle of water spills over the edge.

The walled garden is very warm, the old red brick wall retains the heat and you need to stop for a while and rest. Against the far wall under the shade of a tree is a worn old stone bench. You are glad to be in the shade for a while and sit down on the comfortable cool stone bench, the heady perfume, and the gentle trickle of water take you into a deep relaxed state, you can hear the water in the distance now as you go deeper into relaxation, the coolness is so comforting. The image of a red rose is now in front of you, the perfume, the deep crimson shade, the exact symmetry of each petal folding in on itself, the crimped edge, the dew on the rim, the straight green stem, and again you are filled with that deep emotional sensation. Visualise a person you would like to give this red rose to, hold it out to them as a token of love and light, trust that they are now receiving it.

Take three deep breaths and allow the perfume to linger, to fade, and then it is gone.

You feel the gentle rustle of the breeze as it catches the leaves and you wake to find yourself lying peaceful and calm in your own place on your blanket. Take time to ease yourself back from relaxation. Consider your experience, how you feel mentally, physically and emotionally. All is well.

Ask to Speak to an Angel

In the dark night of the soul, when you are filled with fear and thoughts jump into empty spaces and fill your mind with dread. Ask to speak to an Angel.

Listen in the silence, and open up your heart. Try to still your troubled mind by breathing from the heart. Trust in your feelings, flowing from the heart. Try to console your rapid beating heart,

Feel yourself relaxing now, unwinding from the heart. Feel yourself give in and open up your heart. Make your Angel welcome.

O settle in my heart. Take your wings around me, embrace my troubled heart. Let me feel your touch, inside my lonely heart. Let me feel your breath upon me, soothe my aching heart,

This feeling now is comfort, healing to the heart, that I feel myself surrendering my heart and soul to you in the perfect knowledge that Angels have hearts too.

I Wish I Was A Star

I wish I was a star. If I was a star I would shine and twinkle, I would be the brightest star in the sky. I would start to shine very early in the evening before every other star and I would change my position every night so that some nights I was beside the moon and some nights I could hide behind it, then you would wonder where I was and you would miss me. If I was a star you would think I was dusted with sparkle, I would shimmer so much, I would be so bright and shiny and I would twinkle off and on all the time.

On a dark winter night, I would guide people home who were lost. I would shine in the hills so the farmer could find his lambs. I would shine over the sea so that sailors could find their way home, I would be so high in the sky no one could reach me so I would be very, very safe. Sometimes I would hang out with other stars and we would become clusters and groups, but not every night, sometimes I like to be alone and see how hard I can shine. When I stay still, other stars whiz past me so fast, they call themselves shooting stars.

When people look up into the sky at night they would always say, look at that star how bright it shines. In the summer when the nights are light, I am very high up way beyond the clouds and you cannot see me, but I am still there. When it is pouring with rain I am still there but the rain clouds are hiding me. In the country I shine more brighter still because there are no street light or lights from houses and you can see masses of stars but I still shine the best.

Imagine you are a star. Are you a big shiny star, or a small twinkling star? You are shining silver, sparkling as though you have been dusted with silver light. You are a light, pure and bright. You can shine down from the sky and comfort someone who is lost, you can guide all the lambs home with the shepherd, or you can hang high over the big rough sea and guide the boats into the safe harbour. You can be anywhere you like and because you are so high you shine all over the whole wide world. How proud you are to be so near the moon, together you light up the whole sky.

Sometimes you can meet up with other stars and form a pattern in the sky. Would you like to shine all by yourself tonight, so that someone passing in the street below will look up and say, look at that star isn't it gorgeous? I wonder where it is going and how old it is, how brightly it shines. Tonight is a very clear night for stars and you can shine all night long, everyone will say isn't it a lovely night for stars.

I Wish I Was A Tom Cat

I wish I was a Tom Cat. If I was this cat I would be as black as the night and as big as a dog, I would be the biggest and fastest cat in the neighbourhood and I would be the leader of the pack. All the other cats would follow me because they would know that I could find the best places to go to, especially at night. My eyes would be as big as saucers and shine like the moon on a dark winter's night. My tail would stand upright and be as sleek as silk. All the other cats would say "by, what a fine looking Cat he is". Mice would race into their hidey-holes when they heard me coming, but I would still find ways to catch them.

If I was a Cat, my name would be Burty and I would wear a smart blue collar with my name and address on. I would live in the smartest house in the street and I would be the only pet, as I like to have all my own way. I would have a sheepskin rug for my bed, next to a radiator to keep me warm and snug on the long winter nights when the snow is too deep. I hate snow, my feet get too wet, and the snow makes my body wet, and this makes me feel heavy, and that would mean I couldn't jump up walls and over garden gates.

I have a few girl cats who are my friends, one in particular who I meet on a regular basis her name is Polly. We usually go out during the day as she is not allowed out at night, although I look out for her it seems her owners get very worried when she is out after dark. Maybe this is because she is quite new to the area and doesn't know her way around, when she gets a bit older things might change but at the moment it looks like I will have to stay with the boys, there are a few other girl cats around, but I'm not interested in them.

They seem to be allowed to stay out till all hours of the day or night, and nobody comes looking for them. Some don't even wear a collar with a name and address on, and as for grooming, well a brush has never touched their backs. At least Polly is a regular brushed cat, her fur is mint clean, no fleas on her either, so if I was to snuggle up to her I would know I couldn't catch anything.

Imagine you are a big tom cat, strong, and brave, what colour is your fur, what size is your tail, what colour is your collar? When you go out at night how high can you jump, can you visit places only a cat could squeeze into?. What is your name?

Imagine going out one fine summer night, you could prowl around yards and gardens, go for a stroll in the park, lie on a hammock in someone's garden, sit looking at bees and butterflies, have a doze, wake up, have a sip of water from a friend's pond, visit the local fish shop for a bite to eat, you could jump over garden walls, climb onto roofs, lie on a lawn, get chased by a dog, if you were a cat you could laze in the garden all day and no one will say, what a lazy cat that is, they never will know where you have been, all your adventures would be secrets, when you come home you get a lovely feed and then you can lie down again, this time to dream of lying in the sun on a warm sunny day, stretch out, feel your legs lengthen… feel your back arch. Stretch your paws, roll over, lie still, Purr, Purr, What a lovely Cat you are. What a beautiful Cat you are. Now you are a contented cat, a happy cat, everyone will say, what a beautiful well mannered cat that is.

I Wish I Was A Tap

I know it seems rather a strange thing to want to be, but I am worried about the future, and what will happen when the water runs out? Every time I see those people in far-off lands walking for miles to collect a bucket of water, or even a pan full in the blazing sun, and how careful they are not to spill a drop, I wish I was a tap, and all the water I could save in just one week would help others in the future. Sometime in the future we may be able to give water to everyone, and then the children in far-off lands could go to school and do homework without having to carry water home.

If I was a tap I would only give out a certain amount of water each time I was turned on, for instance when you brush your teeth you only need a trickle, and then another trickle, not a great big whoosh! When you need a bath, you really only need a small amount to cover your legs it doesn't need to come right past your shoulders does it? When you wash the dishes for mum, well sometimes you do, you really only need enough to cover the plates, and rinse the soap off. And do you have to leave the towels on the floor where they all get dirty and end up in the washing basket again?

If I was a tap I would turn myself off after certain hours and take a rest. Where do you think all this water comes from anyway? If it doesn't rain there will be no water in the reservoirs, they will run low, and then become dry and then we may have to go and find water after school, imagine that!

If I was a tap I would be very strict and I would give points for the people who used the least amount of water like reward points at the supermarket. Every time the bill came in, the family could be rewarded, even a competition to find the best water saving family in the country. All the water saved could build a well in a foreign land, a new tap in a village, or even some showers and toilets. Imagine what a difference you could make if you were a tap.

If you were a tap where would you start, with your mum or dad and the car? Look how much water it takes to clean the car. Is it really necessary to wash that car every Saturday, why not every other Saturday ask them? What about the washing, what a lot of water to wash a few clothes, are they really that dirty? What about the garden and that hosepipe on for hours? If you were a tap how long would you give that hosepipe, after all, it might rain tomorrow. And what about that dishwasher, is it full? Can you get another few dishes inside? Check it out and be vigilant. Sometimes these grown-ups can become sloppy and forget about water.

What about water? If you were a tap I bet you would be very strict. Think about it the next time you turn me on, I might not be here for ever you know, and then what will happen. Every time you save a bit of water you are helping the planet, and not just for you now but for people who come after you. Children who aren't even born yet, they will need water, and what will they say, if there's none left, "those greedy people have used all the water and didn't leave any for us". So let's all think about the Tap and give him a rest now and again, I'm sure we can all make a difference.

Of course that's no excuse for not washing your face today!

I Wish I Was A Mermaid

I wish I was a Mermaid. If I was a mermaid I would be able to swim like a fish and dive all the way down to the bottom of the sea. I would have a lovely long tail that would help me to glide through the waves. My body would be blue like the colour of the sea, I would have lovely long golden curly hair and I would never need to get shampoo in my eyes because my hair would never get dirty. I would have slides for my hair and necklaces that I would make out of shells and lots of special treasures that I would find and keep on a secret island where no one could find them.

Around my neck I would have a large shell so I could put it to my ear and hear other mermaids calling me. I would never need to go in the bath because I would always stay clean. I could swim all day long and never get tired. My eyes would be a clear blue, like the colour of the sea, and I would have lovely long eyelashes, in fact I am very, very, pretty. Some people might say I was gorgeous.

If I was a mermaid I would live in a warm turquoise sea beside a coral reef where I could sometimes lie on rock and sunbathe, I would never need to put on sun cream either because my skin is the same as a fish. If I was a Mermaid I would be able to swim to a sandy cove and lie on the golden sand and then I would swim straight out to sea and wash all the sand away.

If I was a Mermaid my best friends would be Dolphins because they are so clever, they are always happy and gentle and they always invite you to play with them. Sometimes they even let you ride on their backs and they take you swimming. They can jump right out of the water, and twirl i the air, they are always smiling and playful They have loads of friends as well and they all play together they never ever fight with each other.

I would have lots of other Mermaids as friends and go swimming together and explore, but swimming with Dolphins is by far the best. Every day would be a holiday. I would swim and play, and always be happy

Imagine you are a Mermaid. Would you like to be a big Mermaid or just a small one? What colour is your hair, is it curly or straight, short or long? What colour are your eyes, is your body the colour of the sea or golden like the sand? Have you a large tail to sweep through the water? Do you have some beautiful beads made out of shells, and a lovely shell to hang around your neck. Have you a secret place to store your treasures? Imagine swimming in the warm blue sea and diving right down to th bottom of it, what treasures you may find.

As you come back up you see some Dolphins in the distance they are calling you to come and play with them, they are calling out your name. See how they smile and encourage you to join in their game jumping through the waves twirling in the air and making that lovely sound that only Dolphins know how to do. They are talking to each other in Dolphin language.

When you feel tired you swim away to your island and lie on the golden sand and let the sunshine warm you, you feel so comfortable and warm and all is safe. Just drift into a lovely sleep, all is quiet.

The sand is soft on your body, it feels like a soft feather cushion, the sun dries your skin and your golden hair, your bed is soft and you just drift into a dreamless sleep.

I Wish I Was A Bird

I wish I was a bird. If I was a bird I would be the biggest seagull in the world. I would have huge wings that would carry me far across the sea. I could even carry my nest with me and move house any time I liked. If I was a seagull I would never build my nest on the side of cliffs, or on a rocky ledge where the sea would lash me off on a stormy night. I have seen other birds who have built their nests on the cliff edge right next door to other birds, the noise is deafening, so many birds screeching and howling, fog horns blaring, the sea banging against the rocks. And the danger. Imagine falling out of the nest when the tide is in and you cannot yet swim. The cold is another thing, it can be freezing on those cliff ledges, the wind whistles around, the rain soaks the nest, the snow settles on your head, the waves lash against the cliff, the spray is all salty and gets in your eyes. The mist and fog settles around you like a damp cold blanket, and the lighthouse shines in your eyes and keeps the chicks awake, no, this is fine in the summer, but raising a family of chicks is a long-term investment and you need security and fair weather. However, there is one plus, food is right on your doorstep and you can do without a babysitter for a few seconds whilst you swoop down to catch a herring or a nice piece of cod for early morning breakfast, take a dip, just chill out, or watch the scenery, but I still feel I need my home comforts, my ideal home, is where I am at this very moment, sitting about a mile away from the sea on a big chimney pot. Now I know this is not very good for the lady who lives here, in fact there have

already been lots of threats to get me evicted, but I am determined to stay. I am protected by some bird law, and that's good enough for me.

This chimney pot is the best in the street, in fact there are six pots on this roof so I can slip between them and build a good sturdy nest, the warmth from the roof is amazing. This is because the house has central heating, and it's on nearly all day, the nest therefore has under floor heating which is great for the chicks. Last year there was a huge problem when I had my family. The lady of the house complained about my feet walking all over the roof, she said I sounded as if I was wearing hob nailed boots. It would sound like that at 5 o'clock in the morning, but I had to get down to the sea early for the fish run, and bring it back in time before the chicks started screaming. Also a fledgling who thought it could fly jumped out of the nest, flew onto the road and couldn't fly back up again. I spent hours in the road trying to pluck her up again, and yes I did attack people, because I thought they were trying to get my baby. Birds are protected too you know, and kidnapping is against the law. I had a hard time last year but I am sticking it out again this year, I refuse to be rehoused on the cliffs at winter. Anyway as soon as the chicks are big enough we have a second home on the cliff but only for the summer months.

Imagine you are a seagull, where would you choose to live? On a big chimney pot or on the cliff edge or perhaps somewhere